Not until you've done your practice!

Not Until You've Done Your Practice!

PHILIP JOHNSTON
ILLUSTRATED BY DAVID SUTTON

A FUTUREPERFECT BOOK

For Katherine, Kate and Laura

NOT UNTIL YOU'VE DONE YOUR PRACTICE!

A FuturePerfect Book

First published in 1990 by Kangaroo Press
Second edition published in 1998 by Kangaroo Press, an imprint of Simon & Schuster Australia
This third edition published in Australia in 2000 by FuturePerfect Publishing
52 Pethebridge Street
Pearce ACT 2607

ISBN 0 646 40265 X

Design by David Sutton
Set in URW Antiqua
Reprinted by BookSurge

10 9 8 7 6 5 4 3 2

Foreword

The battle over practice is almost impossible to win if you tackle it head on, because the situation usually deteriorates into a power struggle between parent and child. You can suggest, you can cajole, you can threaten, but the desire and the application have to come from *within* the student.

That's where this book can help. *Not Until You've Done Your Practice!* begins by assuming that students will not necessarily spend any more time practising than they do already, and then shows them how to achieve much better results in that time.

This increased productivity means that their lessons are more effective, and the praise they receive for their improved performance encourages them to continue to improve. The extra practice then sneaks up on them, as they notice that an extra couple of minutes each day can make a big difference to how much they will impress next lesson. As long as praise from parents and teachers continues to play its part in the circle, the circle will expand.

So *Not Until You've Done Your Practice!* doesn't simply lead the horse to water, it demonstrates how the journey is not only more fun than the horse first suspected, but shorter too.

Equipped with these ideas and with praise from parents and teachers along the way, I believe that the horse won't be able to help itself when it arrives.

Philip Johnston, 2000

Special Note for the third edition

The various editions of *Not Until You've Done Your Practice!* have generated an enormous amount of long-overdue discussion about practising. In the course of seminars and workshops I am often hearing brilliant practising suggestions from other teachers and students, and was tempted for this third edition to be substantially altered to reflect these ideas.

I decided instead to republish this book as the original, and take the new ideas to a website, where they can be updated regularly. Practicespot.com was born because I am not arrogant enough to assume that the best ideas on practising will come from me!

Contents

Part Three: Making it Fun   83

Part Four: Exercises   107

Part One

WHEN?

The Problem

Go on—admit it. You'd rather be eaten by a walrus than practise for half an hour.

Even on a good day, you can probably only concentrate for ten minutes or so—then your mind starts to wander. You imagine how much nicer it would be if you were outside, playing with your friends.

By the time twenty minutes are up, you're probably doing just that. So much for practising.

As a result, you have a big problem—you are supposed to practise for half an hour, but you are sick of it after only ten minutes.

Fortunately, there is a simple solution.

*Even on a good day, most students can only concentrate
for ten minutes or so.*

The Solution

It may take twelve hours of continuous reading to get right through a long novel—but most people would not try to read it in one go. Like the piano student, there's just no way they can concentrate for that long.

So who says that the required half hour of practice needs to be done in one hit? Surely it would be easier to split up this time into two or three shorter practice sessions.

If this were to happen, not only would you get through the half hour with ease, but this half hour would be worth two hours of 'normal practice' simply because you were able to concentrate the whole time.

*Half an hour of non-stop practice can be too much
for some people to take.*

The Routine Method

So three short practice sessions is the answer, and now you must decide when they will take place. One sure way of fitting them in is to make them part of your daily routine.

All you need to do is choose three "landmark events" during the day. Some examples might be:

- having breakfast
- leaving for school
- getting home from school
- your favourite TV show starting

Once you have chosen such events, all you need to do is to decide to practice for ten minutes immediately *before*, or immediately *after* those events.

The combination which I suggest, simply because they are well spaced, is:

- after breakfast

- as soon as you get home from school
- just before dinner

These times may not suit everyone, but that's okay—the beauty of routines is that you can make up one that suits you.

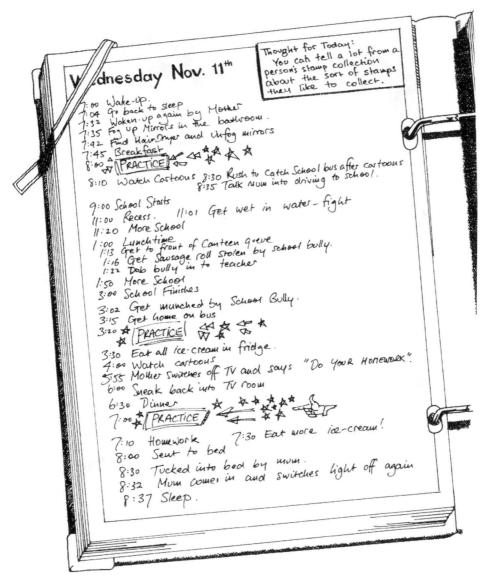

You can make practising part of any routine

The Whenever Method

For those students who can't handle routines, there is another method.

Every day there are countless occasions when you have time to kill. You could be waiting for the rain to stop so you can go outside and ride your bike, watching the paint dry, or wondering when that dial-a-pizza will arrive. Instead of just being bored, grab five minutes of practice.

If you practised every time you had to wait for something, you could notch up hours of practice without tying yourself to a routine, and without cutting in on the time you spend playing with your friends.

Simple, really.

*Every time you have to wait for something, grab
five minutes of practice.*

Peace and Quiet

Before you make any firm decisions about when you are going to practise, remember that it is impossible to practise if you are being distracted.

A distraction might be a loud TV, people moving in and out of the room, or your friends playing outside in the street. Any one of these things is enough to take your mind off the job, let alone all three at once.

For this reason, you must do one of two things before you practise.

First, you could ask your family not to be unnecessarily noisy—just for ten minutes or so. This will mean that before they turn the stereo up, they may remember that you are trying to practise, and leave the volume low. Or they may go around your practice room, rather than through it.

In most cases, all you need to do is ask. (Most parents will be thrilled that you are taking your practice so seriously and will behave themselves very well.)

It is impossible to practise if you are being disctracted.

Second, if there is no way to avoid a distraction, or it would be unreasonable to ask (e.g. if your family's favourite TV show is on when you want to work on your scales), then you must change your practice time.

If you remember these two points, you will be able to practise without being distracted—or driving the rest of your family crazy.

It would be unreasonable to practise during your family's favourite TV show.

Part Two

MAKING IT EASY

Hints that will save you
hours of time

A Little Bit at a Time

A complete piece of music is a frightening thing to look at. There are thousands of strange lines and dots which might as well be in Ancient Assyrian at first glance. No wonder people dislike practising.

An entire page of music is also scary, but much nicer than a whole piece. A line of music is heaps more friendly than a page—and a bar of music is downright easy to learn.

So it seems silly to try and learn a whole piece in one hit. Just as silly as eating the dial-a-pizza by shovelling the whole thing into your mouth at once.

So when you're practising, tackle the piece bar by bar. Before long you will have learnt enough bars to make a line. A little bit longer, and you will have a page.

An old saying is 'take care of the bars, and the piece will take care of itself'.

Just as silly as trying to eat the dial-a-pizza by shovelling the whole thing into your mouth at once.

Repeats

1. Twinkle, twinkle little star
2. How I wonder what you are
3. Up above the world so high
4. Like a diamond in the sky
5. Twinkle, twinkle little star
6. How I wonder what you are

The question is this: if you were to learn to play this tune on the piano, how many lines would you need to learn?

At first glance you would have to say 'six', but is it really?

Look at the first two and the last two lines.

What do you notice? Easy: they are exactly the same. So by learning to play only the first two lines, you can automatically play the last two lines also. You have effectively cut out two lines from your practice.

But that's not all. If you compare the third line with the fourth line, you will notice that they are the same too.

This means you only have to learn one of them, which saves you another line.

Therefore, by looking for repeats, we have cut down the piece from six lines to three—a saving of fifty per cent in time and effort.

I realise that this seems silly in a piece that is only six lines long anyway, but think of what this idea could mean in a piece that is sixty lines long. Almost all pieces of music have repeats in them. Spotting and using them can save you hours of unnecessary practice.

A useful trick to remember.

How many bars is this piece really?

Separate Hands

In any piece of music, the right hand and the left hand parts can be so different from each other that trying to play them together is like trying to rub your tummy and pat your head at the same time. Yet students continue to stagger through practice sessions, trying to play new pieces two hands together immediately.

This is just plain crazy.

If someone were to ask you to juggle and sing the words to 'Greensleeves' at the same time, it would be ridiculous to try to do both if you didn't know any of the words to 'Greensleeves', or if you couldn't juggle. You must perfect the two skills separately before attempting to perform them together.

It is exactly the same for piano playing. Unless you can play the right hand by itself effortlessly, it would be silly to try and add the left hand part (or vice versa).

So when you are practising, make playing two hands together a final stage to be aimed at—not a beginning.

It would be ridiculous to try to juggle and sing 'Greensleeves' at the same time, if you couldn't juggle or didn't know the words.

Slow Practice

Just as silly as trying to play a piece with both hands immediately, is trying to play a piece at full speed straight away.

Like learning to ice-skate, or do a handstand, or ride a bike, new things must be taken slowly at first. Unless you *want* a disaster.

First choose a speed you consider to be very slow. Now halve it, and you should have a sensible practice tempo. From this point you can gradually increase tempo, until you eventually reach full speed. At no stage should you go faster than you can manage—otherwise you will 'trip up' continuously and your practising will be a waste of time.

If you approach your pieces in this manner, speed should never be a problem. A little patience in this department is vital.

*Practising too fast can be a health hazard for you,
your pieces—and your piano!*

Last Time Correct

Although you may not realise it, your practice does not finish when you leave the piano. Your brain will continue to think about the information it picked up during the practice session for a long time afterwards.

For this reason, it is vital that the last time you play something, you play it correctly.

If you do, your brain will remember and work on this correct playing. Chances are that the next time you go to play that particular passage, it will be right.

On the other hand, if you don't make sure that the last playing of a passage is correct, your brain will continue to process the errors afterwards, reinforcing them in your mind. In simple terms this means that the next time you practise, you will probably make the same mistakes as before. And they will be much more difficult to correct.

Once again, observing this hint will save you hours of unnecessary practice.

Your practice does not finish when you leave the piano.

Hard Bits

In almost every piece you play, there will be some parts that you find easy and some that you find hard.

Despite this, most students have a strange tendency to practise all of the piece equally, devoting as much time and effort to the 'easy bits' as they do to the 'hard bits'.

It would seem to me that the 'easy bits' do not require as much practice. In fact, some bars you may find so easy that you need not practise them at all. After all, nobody needs to practise their 'one-times' table.

However, I remember spending a lot of time practising my 'twelve-times' table because it was hard and needed the practice.

So when you are practising, save yourself a lot of wasted time and effort by only practising the 'hard bits'.

Sure, play over the 'easy bits' now and then, just to make sure that they stay easy. But aside from that, you don't really need to worry about them.

Every piece has its hard bits.

Making Things Harder to Make Things Easier

Some sprinters train by tying a rope around their waist, and then a tyre to the other end of the rope. And then they run a hundred metres as fast as they can.

The idea is that since there is no tyre in a real race, they will find it easy by comparison—and probably run better as a result.

You can do the same thing when you are practising.

For example, if your piece needs to go at 132 beats per minute for a school concert, it is probably a good idea to make sure that you can do it at 150 at home. That way you are playing within yourself at the concert, rather than on the edge all the time.

You might want to try practising some sections with your eyes closed, or with no pedal, or while trying to say the alphabet backwards. Anything to make the experience tougher than normal, and then the actual performance will be a breeze.

Of course, you need to be careful only to practise like this sometimes. Otherwise you might get too used to it, and end up actually performing at your school concert with your eyes closed, no pedal and while saying the alphabet backwards...

It is sometimes a good idea to make your practice harder than the real thing...

Fingering

You probably come out of a lot of lessons wondering why your teacher gets so grumpy just because you use the wrong fingers. After all, if you are hitting the right notes, who cares which fingers are doing the job?

There are two very good reasons why you should care.

First, you must remember that the fingering in the music has been worked out by some very clever piano professors who were playing this piece before you were born.

This means that they have spent years working out the easiest possible combination of fingers to play the piece with. And they are telling you—for free—this secret combination.

You'd have to be nuts to ignore it.

Second, if you play a piece with different 'who-cares-which' fingers every time, it is like playing a different piece every time. You will learn the notes more slowly.

Bad fingering is enough to make any teacher grumpy.

And when you have eventually learnt them, they will feel uncomfortable to play.

So it's as simple as this: if you use any old fingers you end up poking at the piano, not playing it.

If you don't believe me, try playing C major scale with the right hand and using these 'who-cares-which' fingers:

C	D	E	F	G	A	B	C
4	3	2	5	1	4	3	2

Hard, isn't it? Your hand probably looked like the one in the picture!

Compare this with the 'proper' fingering (12312345) and you should understand why good fingering is so important.

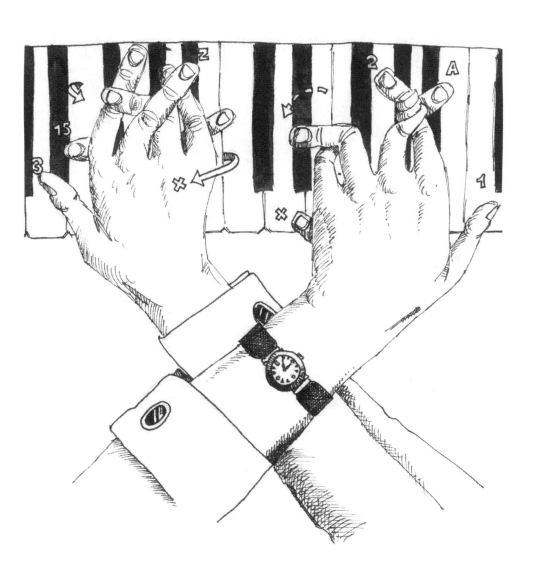

Checking

At some stage you have probably practised a piece quite hard, only to find that your teacher can hear a lot of mistakes that you didn't even know were there. How can there be so many mistakes when you have been practising so hard?

The answer is that you have probably been practising mistakes.

Let's imagine you had to learn the capital cities of the world. One way might be to practise saying over and over, 'The capital of ... is ...'. However, this method will only work if your information is correct. It doesn't matter how long you spend saying 'The capital of England is Brussels', because you still won't get the correct answer in your geography test—even though you may have spent three years practising.

It's exactly the same with your music. If you are playing a bar full of 'E's when the music asks for 'F's, your practice is a waste of time.

The only way around this is to check every so often that what you are playing is the same as what is in the music. And you will have to check carefully, because it is very easy to miss.

Another old saying is 'five minutes of checking can save you hours of doing'.

Memorising: Why?

Many students wonder why they should memorise their pieces. After all, it seems like rather a lot of trouble for no particular gain.

Not true. There are some exciting benefits for people who can play without needing to look at the music.

First, there are times when it is necessary to watch your hands in order to hit the correct notes, and you can't do this if your eyes are glued to the music.

Second, as soon as you start playing pieces of any length, you will have to turn pages. Unless you have a third arm, it is almost impossible to turn a page without interrupting the piece.

In either case there would be no problem if you didn't have to rely on the music.

A bonus is that people think playing a piece without the music is terribly clever, like being able to do a handstand or something.

If these people were to read the next pages, they'd realise that it isn't so difficult after all.

Memorising: How?

There are two very simple ways to memorise a piece:

1. Step by step

Break up the piece into sections of about two bars each. You are going to start with the first section so forget about the rest of the piece for the moment. Play these bars over and over with the music. Unless you can play these two bars easily with the music, you will not be able to memorise them.

Once you are expert at playing these two bars with the music, try them without it. If you make a mistake or forget, don't worry—just go back to the music and play over a few times from where you got stuck. Then try again. After a while you will be able to play these two bars from memory.

Then try the next section, using the same method. Even if you memorise only four bars a day using this method, that adds up to a whole page within a week.

2. Random method

With this method play the piece using the music, but watch your hands whenever you feel able. At first that may only be for the odd note, but as time goes by you will find that the sections where you can watch your hands will get longer.

Using this method, you will randomly fill in the whole piece with little sections where you are watching your hands instead of the music. If you persist you will eventually be able to watch your hands while playing the whole piece. Congratulations—you have memorised it!

Picking Up

If you make a mistake and get completely lost while you are playing a piece, you can either go right back to the beginning and start again, or you can pick up from where you left off and keep going.

It is much less painful for you and your audience if you don't have to go all the way back to the start, so it is very useful to be able to pick up from anywhere.

However, like everything else, picking up takes practice: you can't expect to be able to pick up from anywhere the very first time you try it.

Once you feel comfortable with playing a piece, try starting from the second line, instead of the first. Then try from the third line, and so on. Eventually you will be able to pick up from virtually anywhere in the piece (at least to the nearest two or three bars).

As well as being able to save yourself gracefully if you do make a mistake in performance, you will also find that your playing of the piece has improved.

And in an exam or concert, this ability will place you in a different league from the poor person who has no choice except to go back to the start in the event of a mishap.

Pressure Playing

There are a lot of students who play beautifully at home and at lessons, but take them to an exam room, or put them on a stage and they fall apart. The reason is that they are not used to playing under pressure.

But like everything else that you wish you could do, but can't, playing under pressure will get better with practice. The best way would be to have four hundred exams and concerts each year, but since this is impossible you must put yourself under pressure while you are practising at home.

One way is to imagine that the practice session is a concert and there are one thousand people listening. Walk to your piano, bow, and play your piece as though this is the real thing. This idea may sound silly, but if you imagine and concentrate enough, you can get quite nervous about your imaginary audience.

If you do this often enough, you will find that on real occasions the idea of playing in front of an audience will be somehow familiar. And you will play much better as a result.

There are many more ways of putting yourself under pressure—you can invent some for yourself with a little imagination, or you can consult the Games section, where you will find some games that are designed to give you practice at playing under pressure.

Warming Up

When you play the piano, you are expecting your fingers to behave like well tuned athletes: they must be able to move quickly and with precision.

If you have ever watched any sport, you will notice that players don't just jump off the bus and on to the field. They warm up first.

You should too. If you want to be able to play well at a lesson, exam or even when just practising, your hands must be warm first.

The best way to warm up is to play some music very slowly, whether it's scales, pieces or the do-it-yourself exercises at the back of this book. You will find that after a little while the stiffness will go and you will be able to do yourself justice when you play.

If you want to play well at a lesson, exam, or even when practising, your hands must be warm first.

Metronome Magic

You would probably like to set fire to your metronome—I always wanted to—but you would be destroying a vital practice tool with countless uses.

The most obvious use—and probably the only way you have used it—is to keep yourself in time. So if you find in lessons that you are speeding up and slowing down all over the place, then it is time to practise your piece with the metronome. You will find that keeping in time with the ticks will sort out the problem very quickly indeed.

But this is only a drop in the ocean.

You probably have some pieces that you can play well slowly, but which fall apart at high speed. The metronome will fix this problem, too.

All you have to do is set the metronome at a slow speed that you can cope with.

If you play your piece easily at this speed, then move the metronome up one notch (about 4 beats per minute).

You won't notice this slight increase in speed and will cope very easily as a result. You also won't notice the next increase, or the next.

By increasing the speed gradually, you will get to the speed you want with relative ease. And you can really only increase speed gradually and reliably enough with a metronome.

A metronome is also a very good test of how well you know a piece: the parts you don't really know will come out as mistakes when you use the metronome. It's much better that you find these parts with a metronome than discover them during a performance.

There are countless other uses, from checking the tempo of a piece, to keeping your slow practice slow.

It is always immediately obvious to teachers which students use a metronome—simply because they play better. Please don't burn it.

You would probably like to destroy your metronome—I always wanted to.

How to do an Extra Sixty Hours of Practice in a Year Without Even Trying

Sixty hours of extra practice in a year? Your pieces would sound awesome!

But who has time to do that?

You do. It's much easier than you think.

You see, ten minutes every day adds up to 3,650 minutes in a year. Which is actually over sixty hours altogether.

So all you really need to do is find an extra ten minutes to practice every day, and those sixty hours of extra practice are yours.

Not so hard, and you will not believe how much better you will be playing.

P.S. Just work out how much extra practice that comes to if you were to do twenty minutes of extra practice every day! I think you will be amazed... and it's the reason that the students who know this easy trick sound so good.

$$p_1 = \left(\propto \frac{360 x^{-i\pi} c^{2\theta}}{\not X \pm \infty} \right) + \frac{\sqrt[3]{5\pi \varepsilon + \partial y}}{(z \to z^2 + \varepsilon)} - 16\, rtf$$

$$= xc \int_{\pi^{x+\beta}}^{e\log\alpha} \left(x + \frac{y^{5l}r\theta}{vip} \right) - 7dy \sum\nolimits_{cp}^{lp} x \to h''$$

$$\approx \left(\theta \left[cd + \frac{penguin\,\pi}{257 \pm x^{23}} + \propto \xrightarrow{legato} \Omega \right] - 1 \right)$$

$$\therefore p_2 = \sqrt{\infty \pm zx^2} - vhs \times \left(56x' \frac{ei\gamma}{\musicalnote} \right) - \tfrac{1}{2}$$

$$= 60 \text{ hours more practice/year}$$

Sixty extra hours is not as complicated as you might think...

When Your Piano Sounds Sick

Since it is actually cheaper to buy a small house than it is to buy a concert Steinway, chances are that your piano at home might not be exactly state-of-the-art.

Bad pianos can be frustrating—notes that go down and won't come up again, notes that are not in tune, pedals that don't work properly, and sometimes even notes that make no sound at all.

However, if your piano is doing some of these things, there is something you can do that is much cheaper than buying a new Steinway.

Simply have your parents call your piano tuner and make sure he or she has a look at it at least once a year, preferably every six months.

They can make a big difference to how your piano sounds, and that can make your practising a much nicer experience. It is hard for you to sound good if your piano *can't* sound good.

Bad pianos can be frustrating... it's hard for you to sound good if your piano can't sound good.

Counting Your Way Out of Trouble

Working out rhythms can be very tricky. There are crotchets, quavers, minims, semibreves, semiquavers, dotted semi-quavers, double-dotted-demi-semi-quavers... but if music were nothing but crotchets, nobody would listen to it.

There really are only three ways of making sense of all these note values.

The first method is to guess. Use the Force. Play notes when you think it feels 'right'. Maybe you'll get lucky, but I don't think so. This method is not a good idea unless you like your teacher pulling faces while you play.

The second method is to get somebody else to play it for you and then copy what you hear. But remember, your teacher does not live at your house so unless you have a recording handy, that probably can't happen.

So the only method that is left to you is to count while you play. That way you can work out exactly when each note should happen, and ensure that they make their entrance at the right time.

Remember, the right note at the wrong time is still a wrong note (and vice-versa, of course).

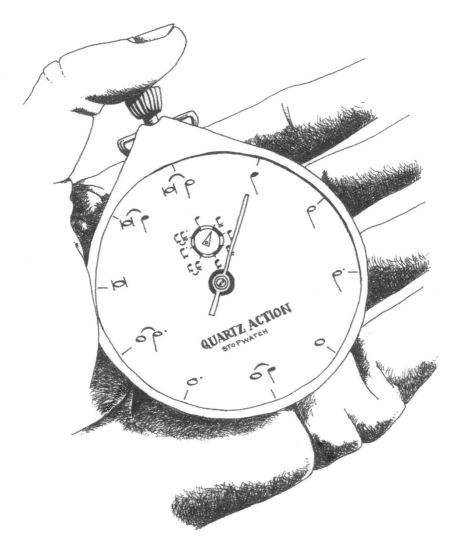

Working out rhythms can be very tricky... unless you are counting of course.

Experimenting

A famous astronomer once said that there are more different ways to play a piece than there are grains of sand on all the beaches in the world.

Some of these ways will be brilliant. Some of them will be so bad that your audience will most probably burst out laughing.

Let's imagine that you only ever play your piece one way. You might be happy with it, but there might be better ways of performing it that you have never even thought of.

You won't know unless you try. Experiment—what would happen if the left hand was louder than the right hand during the repeat? What would happen if you made your 'p's really quiet, and didn't get carried away by your 'ff's? What would happen if the whole thing was a shade faster? What would happen if you watched your right hand instead of your left hand during that difficult bit? What would happen if you moved your wrist a lot during the staccato section instead of keeping it still?

If you knew the answers to all these questions, and a hundred others that you will think of, you could make your piece sound much better.

And there is no way of knowing these answers unless you experiment.

Apart from being so useful, experimenting is so much fun that you will wonder why you never did it in your practice before.

You won't discover the best way to play a piece
unless you experiment.

Staying Relaxed

If you have ever watched Olympic athletes running, you have probably noticed that everything is so effortless and relaxed that it almost looks as though they are not even trying.

Don't be fooled. They are trying just as hard as they can. But they have discovered that you perform better if you can stay loose. They know that screwing up your face and tensing all your muscles actually makes you run slower, not faster.

The same is true in your playing. A lot of students react to hard bits by making their arms and wrists tight.

This is craziness. All it does is make the hard bits impossible.

So whenever you are struggling with a hard bit, check to make sure that you are as relaxed as you can be.

Not only will it make your piece easier, but you will run less risk of actually hurting yourself while you are practising.

You will play much better if you can stay
relaxed while you practise.

Four Things That Hard Bits Hate

If there is a hard bit that is giving you a hard time, the best thing to do is give it a hard time.

What most people don't realise is that in the same way that vampires don't like garlic and wicked witches in the *Wizard of Oz* are dissolved by water, there is a secret list of things that hard bits hate. Expose them to these things and they shrivel up and die, leaving you with just good bits.

So, to teach hard bits a lesson, here is the secret list of Four Things That Hard Bits Hate (you could probably guess some of these things if you have been reading this book carefully):

1. Practise the hard bit *slowly*. Hard bits love it when you play fast, but turn pale when the tempo is not so hot.

2. Practise the hard bit using *separate hands*. All hard bits fear this. They are much more comfortable if you

are too busy playing two hands together to notice them.

3. Shine a light on the hard bit—practise it and nothing else. They would much rather hide in the dark than have anyone paying this much attention to them.

4. Practise the hard bit *lots and lots of times*. The more times you do it, the smaller the hard bit gets until it eventually is too small to see—or hear.

So don't just sit there. Go get them... before they get you.

If a hard bit is giving you a hard time,
you should give it a hard time.

Details

A lot of people think that when they have learned the notes and fixed the counting that they have finished.

They are happy if they can simply press the right buttons at the right time.

So are typists. And there should be a big difference between typing and playing the piano.

If all you do is play the right notes, then you will be ignoring staccatos and phrasing marks. You won't bother with accents or fermatas, ritenutos or accelerandos. You'll leave out the da capos and a tempos, and forget completely about turns and trills.

It is a bit like thinking that driving a car is only about using the accelerator and the steering wheel at the right times. It means you don't use the windscreen wipers or the indicators, gears or the brake. You ignore the rear vision mirrors and forget about your seat belt. You just drive. Into things, mostly.

If you find that you don't know what some of the signs mean, ask your teacher.

Composers think details are just as important as the notes—in fact, they really are notes. If you wouldn't dream of leaving out all the sharps and flats in a piece, then you shouldn't ignore the other details either.

Head Down, Four Hours and Trust...

Some pieces just feel as though they are not getting any better, no matter how much practice they seem to get.

The temptation then is to practice something else, or worse still, stop practising altogether.

If you are feeling frustrated like that about one of your pieces, try this:

First, get a tape recorder and record your piece. Right now. Warts and all. Given that this piece has been driving you crazy, you probably won't win a Grammy for the result.

Then go and do a total of four hours practice on it. (No, silly, not all at once—do four hours *altogether* on it over the next week or so.)

Once that four hour total has been reached, record it again.

Then play back both versions. I think you will be pleas-antly surprised by the comparison.

You see, intelligent practising always makes your pieces better—it's just that sometimes watched pots seem to take a long time to boil.

Head down, four hours of work on it altogether, trust that it is improving a little bit all the time, and it will.

Deciding What to Practise

Okay, so you have got a list in front of you of things your teacher wants you to do for next week:

C, G, D and A major scales, separate hands. A and E minor both hands together. Check the fingering of the Czerny etude. Learn the LH of the first movement of the Clementi Sonatina, the RH of the second movement of the Kuhlau, and iron out the rhythm problems in your Kabalevsky. And then in the time you have left over, there is the top part of a duet to learn for a concert in April...

Arggh! Where do you start? How are you going to get all of that done?

There are a few things you can try that might help.

CREATE A ROSTER

This is a method a lot of students use. Simply write out the days of the week, and then underneath each day note the things that you will cover on that day. So on Monday you might do D and A Major, learn the first half of the LH for the Clementi and spend some time working out how to count the Kabalevsky. Tuesday is Kuhlau and the minor scales. Wednesday is the duet and more Clementi... you get the idea. Just make sure that everything your teacher asked for gets covered a few times during the week.

THE PLAYTHROUGH AND FIX ON THE RUN

This method means you pull out one of your required pieces or scales and try to play it through from beginning to end. As soon as you get to a bit that you have trouble with, stop, go over that bit until you can do it and then move on to a different piece. You will visit each piece many times during the week, hopefully stopping at a new place each time.

THE RANDOM METHOD

Seven things to do? First, give each task a number. (Major scales might be 1, Kuhlau 2, Clementi 3 and so on.) Then get a pack of playing cards and pick out all the aces through to the sevens. Shuffle that pile of cards, take the top card and look at it. The number will tell you what item to work on, and by the time you have worked your way through the whole pile (which may take a week of practice), you will have covered each task four times.

TOUGHEST THINGS FIRST

Rank those seven things from easiest to hardest. You begin your practice with the toughest piece and then work your way down the list.

So if you are terrified of minor scales but think Czerny is a doddle, then minor scales will be one of the first things your work on, with the Czerny being left until the end.

Having read through these methods, you might decide that you want to try several of them. Nothing wrong with that, and hopefully the changes will help keep your practising interesting.

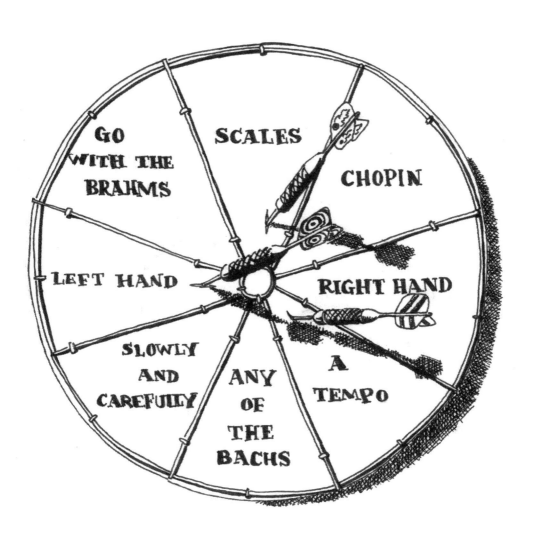

Balance

Most piano pieces have got lots of notes all happening at the same time. Some of these notes make up the tune. Some of these notes are the accompaniment.

Telling which is which can be very difficult for the audience if the performer plays them all as though they are all equally important.

Worse still, if you play the accompaniment part too loudly, you will bury the tune underneath lots of notes—and you might never find it again.

Audiences love tunes, and if they can't find them easily they stop listening. So help them out a little bit by *balancing* your playing—make sure the tune is easy to hear, and that the accompaniment is in the background.

Otherwise it would be like watching a play where there is a spotlight on all the characters at once, even the actors with non-speaking parts. You wouldn't know who to watch, so you probably wouldn't watch anybody.

When you are playing you create *aural spotlights* by playing some things more loudly than others. It's known as *balance* and makes the audience listen to the parts you want them to hear.

A trick too powerful not to use.

Dynamics

If someone ever says that they are having trouble sleeping, you can easily help them.

Just play them one of your pieces — but make sure you play it at the same volume from beginning to end. No loud sections, no soft sections, just all... exactly... the... YAWN... same... night-nights... zzzzzzz...

instead of applause at the end of your piece, you will hear snoring. Truly.

Music is amazingly boring unless you sometimes change how loudly you are playing.

The special word for all the instructions in the music that tell you how loudly to play is 'dynamics'. The composer puts them in to help make their music as interesting as it possibly can be.

But it's no good just looking at the dynamics on the page. You actually have to make them happen.

Otherwise, you may have to tiptoe out of the room very quietly at the end of your concerts.

It would be rude to wake up all those people in the audience.

How to Make Your Piece Sound Really Bad, Even Though You are Practising Three Hours a Day

It's not easy, but we have a list of instructions here if you really would like to try...

1. Always practise the piece by playing from the very beginning all the way to the end. Don't stop for anything. Especially not mistakes or hard bits.

2. Always practise the piece as fast as you can. Get a stopwatch out and see if you can break your old record each time. Music is all about Personal Bests.

3. Don't ever look at the music or check the notes, or count the rhythms. You're clever. You can guess them.

4. Use whichever fingers you like. Perhaps you could make a pattern (why not your phone number?) and use those fingers in that order all the way through the piece. For even better results, use the same finger all the way through (2–2–2–2–2–2–2 is good).

5. Choose your favourite dynamic level and play at that level all the way through the piece. To make sure people are listening properly, choose 'fffff'.

6. Don't worry about rests or staccatos or stuff like that. They're just little details and don't really make that much difference.

7. Put a TV set on your piano. If some people can drink coffee and watch TV at the same time, then why can't you do some practice and see *The Simpsons* at the same time?

8. Always learn your pieces two hands together straight away.

9. Practice two hundred different pieces in the same week. Be careful not to spend more than thirty-five seconds on each one. Variety is the spice of life.

10. Ignore the hard bits. Play the easy bits over and over. After all, it's important to sound good all the time while you are practising.

11. Only practice when you are very sleepy, or when other people are trying to sleep. Then play as loudly as you possibly can to keep yourself focused.

(The authors of *Not Until You've Done Your Practice!* accept no responsibility for any damage that may arise to you, yourself or your piano teacher should you actually be silly enough to try any of these ideas...)

Part Three

MAKING IT FUN

Games and fun ideas that will turn your practice into something to look forward to

Reasons

Practising can be deadly boring if you are doing it for the wrong reasons. Sitting at the piano because your parents insist is a silly reason. So is practising just because your teacher told you to do half an hour every day.

However, practising because you tell yourself to is a good feeling.

This way, you avoid the nagging and the 'bad' lessons, and end up actually enjoying your time at the piano. And your playing will get much better as a result.

On the next few pages you will find reasons to practise that will make your practice fun.

They are probably the most important pages for you in this book.

Sitting at the piano because your parents insist
is a silly reason.

Rewards

In your life, you will have to do lots of things that you don't enjoy. It might be doing a spelling test, eating brussels sprouts—or practising.

However, these bad things don't seem half as bad if you do something which is fun straight after them. A maths test just before you play at lunch time is much better than a test at the start of the day. Brussels sprouts followed by ice-cream are much nicer than brussels sprouts on their own.

Similarly, practising followed by something you really enjoy doing is much more fun.

So next time, before you start to practise, promise your-self a treat when you have finished (on the condition that you do all the practice you are supposed to).

This is an important step towards making practising fun.

Before you practise, promise yourself a treat for when you have finished.

Targets

Once you actually want to practise, the practice itself can be much more fun if you have some targets in mind.

A target is just something you want to get done in a session. It might be to learn the right hand of the first four bars of your new piece. Or it might be to get a particular tricky bit right with some slow metronome practice.

As long as your targets are sensible (don't make them too hard), you will see yourself achieving something every practice session—and that is a great feeling.

You might want to keep a list of your targets and tick them off as you can do them. At the end of the week you will have quite a long list of new things that you can do.

So from now on, don't sit down at the piano just to 'do some practice': set yourself a target and practise with a purpose.

Charts

All you have to do is buy a large sheet of cardboard and some stickers.

Every time you practise for a ten minute block, put a sticker on the chart. Make sure you put the stickers on in neat rows: they will be easier to count.

Then you just need to talk to your parents about a reward for a certain amount of stars. For example, you might get a pocket money bonus for twenty stars. Or a trip to the zoo for fifty stars. Two hundred stars and you might be looking at a new skateboard.

This is a great way of making yourself want to practise; after all, nobody will be able to drag you away from the piano if your very own helicopter is only 114,336 stars away.

Using charts will make you see prices in a different way.

Card Games

If you have a piece that you know reasonably well, but would like to know backwards, then card games are for you.

PREPARING CARD GAMES

The first step is to divide your piece into four equal sections, called A, B, C and D. Label these sections on the music in pencil, so that you know where they are.

Next you need twelve small squares of paper. Below, you will find a list of twelve instructions. Write one instruction on each card.

A Left Hand, A Right Hand, A Together, B Left Hand, B Right Hand, B Together, C Left Hand, C Right Hand, C Together, D Left Hand, D Right Hand, D Together.

Now put all the cards in an ice-cream container, mix them up—and you are ready to play.

PLAYING CARD GAMES

1. Empty the ice-cream container!

Draw a card (without looking) from the ice-cream container. Now look at the card, and do what it says (e.g. A Right Hand means play section A with the right hand only).

If you make a mistake of any sort you must do what the card says again, and then put the card back in the ice-cream container.

If you play it without any slips put the card on top of the piano.

The game, and your practice session, is over when the ice-cream container is empty.

So the better you play, the sooner you can stop.

2. Scored ice-cream

Simply play as in 1, but every time you have to put a card back into the ice-cream container add one to your score. The lower your score, the better. If your score is zero, then you are so good at this piece that you should choose one you find a little harder. Otherwise it's a bit like playing darts with a board that covers the whole wall.

3. Diced ice-cream

Once again, when your game is over, so is the session. This time, roll a die as you draw a card to find out how many times you must do what it says. When you have got through all twelve cards in this manner, the game is over.

4. Lotsa-ice-cream

For this all you need do is draw up some extra cards.

Some possible extras might be: A and B Right Hand; B and C Right Hand; C and D Right Hand; A, B and C Right Hand; B, C and D Right Hand; The Whole Lot Right Hand... and so on for the Left Hand and Together.

If there is a section you are having particular trouble with, you may want to draw up some repeats of existing cards so that you cover it two or three times in the course of your game.

Pressure Games

These games are designed to give you practice at performing under pressure. They are only for pieces that you are very sure of.

1. Twice is nice

Use the practice cards for this game. When you draw a card, you must be able to do what the card says twice in a row with no mistakes. Until you do this, you cannot go on to the next card...

So even if you play it perfectly the first time and make a teensy-weensy mistake on the very last note of your second play-through, you must start all over again from the first play-through because of the twice in a row rule.

And until the ice-cream container is empty, you cannot stop practising.

So if you concentrate hard and play well, you could be finished after only twenty-four short sections. If you make a mess of things however, you could be there until the turn of the century.

That's pressure.

2. Thrice is nice

This game is only for those who are very sure of their piece, or those who have nothing better to do for a few weeks.

It works just the same as 'Twice is Nice', only this time it has to be three times in a row with no mistakes.

Good luck.

3. Come 'n' hear it

For this, you will need a volunteer from your family. Start your practice with section A. When you feel it is good enough, ask your volunteer to come and hear it. If they pick up any mistakes or hesitations, they will go away and come back in five minutes to hear it again. Until they hear A played perfectly, you cannot go on to B. Until they have heard successful performances of all the sections, you cannot leave the piano.

Once again, this is only for those who know their piece very well.

A member of the family can put some extra pressure on you.

4. Come 'n' tape it

This is a good pressure game for when you have no family volunteers. You will need the practice cards, a tape recorder and a blank tape. Draw a card and tape your efforts at doing what the card says. Then draw another one and tape it too.

Once you have got through all the cards, listen to the tape. Every card that was played perfectly may be put on the piano. The remainder are to be put back in the ice-cream container, so that you can play 'Twice is Nice' with them. What fun.

...of course you can make up your own pressure games.

Seven Stages of Misery

This game is really nasty.

First you need to imagine seven different locations on the top of your piano, with the first location being on the far left, the last being on the far right. You will need a token of some sort to move from location to location, because now your piano is set up like a giant board game.

Your token starts at the first location, which is known as 'Stage 1'. The aim of the game is to advance your token to 'Stage 7'.

You play a section of your piece that needs work once. If you manage that with no mistakes, you advance your token to Stage 2.

If you make any mistakes at all, you go back one stage. (The furthest you can go back is the beginning. So if you make a mistake when you are still on Stage 1, there is no penalty.)

Then you play the section of your piece again, note whether it was mistake-free or not, move your token either forwards or backwards as a result, and so on. When your token gets to Stage 7, the game—and your practice session—are over. But not until then. And that is why this game is so deadly.

You see, you might work hard for half an hour and get to Stage 6, but then you will start to get a little nervous, because you are close to winning.

The nerves cause you to make a little mistake. Back to Stage 5. That makes you impatient, so you try it again, only faster. Whoops. Back to Stage 4. Getting mad with the piece then causes more mistakes and you go down to Stage 3. From Stage 3 to Stage 1 seems to take only a few seconds and you are back where you started, with half an hour of work down the drain.

I think your grandparents would describe the whole experience as 'character-building', but we think you have to be a special sort of crazy to want to play this game very often.

Part Four

EXERCISES

Scales, arpeggios and do-it-yourself exercises

Scales and Arpeggios

Sooner or later, you will be given scales and arpeggios to practise—and you will probably wonder why. After all, they're not very exciting to play or listen to, so why bother?

The reason is this: almost every piece you play will have scales and arpeggios hidden in it. As soon as you have a melody with lots of notes rising or falling by steps, you are actually playing a scale. As soon as you have a section which moves upwards or downwards in leaps, you are playing an arpeggio.

So if you are good at playing scales and arpeggios to begin with, these sections in the piece will be easy, leaving only small parts of the piece which you really need to work on.

Once again, it's a case of saving yourself hours of work.

If you were good at scales and arpeggios, your pieces would need hours less practice. That's enough to make anyone happy.

Making Scales and Arpeggios Bearable

No matter how useful scales and arpeggios are to you, practising them can be deadly boring, if you go about it the wrong way. Most students simply sit there and play a scale up and down and up and down and up and down and up... see? It's boring. So once you have learnt the notes and fingering of the exercises, vary how you play them:

- you can play them slow, or fast;
- you can play them loud or soft;
- you can change the rhythm and play them in triplets, or dotted rhythms, or whatever you can think of;
- you can play them with one hand or two hands;
- or one, two, three or four octaves;
- you can play them a third, a sixth or a tenth apart;

- you can play one scale in one hand and a different one in another (this doesn't sound too pretty, but it is a great test of how well you know them);
- you can make cards for your scales and arpeggios and play one of the card games with them;
- use your imagination: have combinations of the ideas above, or make up your own variations.

The trick is to make sure you don't practise them the same way all the time—they sure won't appear in your pieces the same way all the time and you will probably enjoy doing them a lot more.

Do-It-Yourself Exercises

As well as scales and arpeggios, exercises are very useful for making your fingers stronger and cleverer. There are plenty of exercise books on the market, but it is much more fun (not to mention cheaper) to make up your own.

The best way to design an exercise is to choose a hard bit from one of your pieces. Once you have chosen it, ask yourself exactly what makes this bit hard—it might be a trill, or a big stretch in one of the hands, or repeated notes. Once you know what it is, you're ready to make an exercise.

Let's pretend that the hard bit was hard because of a jump of a tenth (an octave plus two notes) in the right hand. Your exercise will be made up of tenths. Maybe you will jump from C to E four times, then D to F four times, and so on. Or you might want to do each jump just once.

You might want to do this jump over and over in triplets.

You are limited only by your imagination.

You will find that when you come back to the hard bit, it will seem much easier than it was before.

Exercises are a very useful way for making your fingers stronger and cleverer.

A Final Word

You now know lots of little tricks to save hours of practice time. This means you can be out playing with your friends much sooner.

But that's not all. Now that you know about practice games, you can play while you practise.

You see? Practising can be fun—if you go about it the right way. The funny thing is, this holds true for most things that you don't like doing. Think about that.

So what are you waiting for?

Index

Wherever on the planet you do your practice...

Help is at hand

www.practicespot.com

The world's largest website for music teachers and students

The Practice Revolution

Getting great results from the six days *between* music lessons

The most ambitious guide to practicing ever undertaken—over 320 pages of what works, what doesn't, what really happens when students practice, and how to fix it. *The Practice Revolution* seeks to end forever the obsession with how much practice students do, and switches the focus to helping students get more done in less time.

"This book is perhaps in the top 1% of all of the things I have ever recommended. Every sentence is new and important and this goes on for 321 pages... if teachers were to absorb the content there would, indeed, be a revolution in teaching and learning. Buy the book!"
    —*Canadian Music Educator Association Journal*

"...idea-studded book on the whole practice process... when that student leaves, it should be with the practice skills to work alone. Johnston has generously outlined hundreds of ways to do that."
    —*California Music Teacher Magazine*

"This is simply the best book ever written on the techniques of effective practice for musicians. The chapters are detailed. Every page gives important, indispensable tips"
    —Review at *amazon.com*

"... first-rate. After reading only half the book, I believe it had a positive impact on my teaching... Consider both buying the book and stock in the company!"
    —*Horn Call* (Journal of the International French Horn Society)

"...a great success... a valuable resource for studio teachers in its wealth of strategy and stimulus to creativity"
    —*American Music Teacher*

order online from www.practicespot.com